Specimen Sight-Reading Tests for Recorder

Descant and Treble

Grades 1-5

The Associated Board of
the Royal Schools of Music

© 1995 by The Associated Board of the Royal Schools of Music AB 2465

AB 2465

4 Allegretto

5 Andante

6 Moderato

7 Allegretto

AB 2465

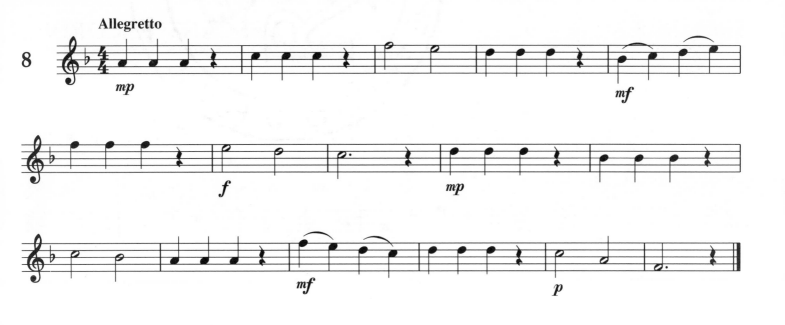

GRADE 2

Lively

5

Andante

6

Allegretto

7

Dancing

8